S

4.95

Distributed by

Motorbooks International
Publishers & Wholesalers Inc.

Osceola, Wisconsin 54020, USA

Other Books By James Neal Blake

* *Songs, Scenes and Street Cries*

RUN YOUR CAR ON SUNSHINE:

USING SOLAR ENERGY
FOR A SOLAR POWERED CAR

By
James Neal Blake, Ph.D.

———— SECOND PRINTING ————

Copyright© 1980 by James Neal Blake
Cover Art by: Dennis E. Smith
Illustrations by: Dennis E. Smith

Poems on pages 6 and 61
by James Neal Blake

Published by:
LOVE STREET BOOKS
P.O. BOX 58163
Louisville, Kentucky 40258 U.S.A.

Library of Congress Catalog Number: 80-82734
ISBN   Paperback Edition   0-915216-65-5
ISBN   Hardback Edition   0-915216-64-7

This publication is intended as a general, informal, often theoretical commentary of thoughts on solar energy toward a solar powered car. It presents the author's speculative opinions in regard to the material covered. The author, the publisher, and the bookseller specifically disclaim any personal liability; loss, or risk incurred as a result of the use of (mis)application, either directly or indirectly, of ideas expressed in this monograph.

The reader is urged to pursue technical information of the applied type and its valid and reliable construction and application from the appropriate consulting firms and professional technicians, some of which sources are listed in the appendix of references.

Totem

The
People
Laugh
And
Deride
The
Ancients
And
They
Cry —
"See how naive and superstitious were the primitive minds
who worshipped the sun and the base elements of the
earth?" And they laugh on but they do not see
How
They
Themselves
Are
Made
From
These
Base
Elements
And
Are
Still
Very
Much
Dependent
On
The
Basic
Solar
Energy
Of
The
Sun.

CONTENTS

SOLAR POWERED CARS TODAY

The Israelis have developed one with a flat-plate collector under the hood; and they'll probably run it well and bring it to a high level of refinement and ultimate efficiency under the radiant energy of the desert Sun.

The December, 1978 issue of *The Engineer* reports that "Rolls-Royce were the overall winners," in a brief article entitled, "Rolls-Royce wins the solar car race in championship style." The article further states that over 60 companies submitted a car for the race and more than 120 had applied for solar cells and motors. Whether serious or in sporting fun the article suggests possibilities.

The Solar Energy and Energy Conversion Laboratory of the University of Florida converted a GM Corvair to a solar-electric powered vehicle. This vehicle has a novel transistorized field excitation system for variable speed control and regenerative braking to improve the overall power conversion efficiency. This conversion was reported on at the "International Congress On The Sun In The Service Of Mankind," Unesco House, Paris, France (2 July 1973).

What are we waiting on?

Let's run the cars on Sunshine!

SOLAR POWER IS THE ANSWER
TO THE FUEL SHORTAGE

One of the things we must keep in mind when we talk of initiating solar engine development for solar powered automobiles is that it will take time, research, experience and ultimately some discoveries in order to refine the necessary engine parts to a point where they will be able to provide the level of performance and efficiency to which we are accustomed in our current gasoline powered vehicles. We need to keep two things in mind where our gasoline powered vehicles are concerned. First of all, the original ones were considered by many people, to be inferior and undependable for comparison to the horse and carriage. The original Model T Fords and other first cars were laughed at, derided and they lacked credibility. (The horse farms, carriage builders, harness shops, and blacksmith shop businesses undoubtedly felt very threatened!) Not only did the original gasoline powered automobiles have a long way to go in comfort and appearance, they didn't go very fast either. It hasn't been all that many years ago that 30 and 40 m.p.h. was considered fast (!) for automobiles.

There are some interesting and reputable electric cars on the market today that can go that fast and they are certainly comfortable to ride in. If sufficient research and governmental and industrial complexes were to combine serious effort (forgetting the lobbyists' interests; the self-vested interests of controlling companies with the built-in laws, public, social and economic), it might be amazing to find what we would have in a genuine solar-powered service car.

I wish to emphasize that we should expect that any beginning makes or early models of solar-powered cars would have, in the beginning, certain drawbacks and disadvantages compared to the gasoline powered vehicles we use. After all, it has taken nearly 80 or more years to develop their current performance advantages — they should be good — but! — they were *not* all that efficient, comfortable and chic in the beginning. Furthermore, if we don't get realistic and accept a truly advantageous long range alternative for powering our cars, we are not going to be driving them long as they are now anyway. First, most of us can't afford it at today's gasoline prices and nearly all countries of the world are expressing utmost concern over the fact that the energy resources needed for powering them, oil, etc., is simply running out. There simply doesn't seem to be any way we can continue to put off developing an automobile that will use the most available, least expensive and most plentiful resource for its fuel or power. And that energy source must needs be, by the best of analysis at the present time, none other than *solar energy.*

The Stirling Engine
and
Converting Solar Energy
To Power

The United States Department of Energy has outstanding published documents which the serious reader will want to peruse. Some of these are identified and listed in the bibliography of this monograph. One document, *A Technology Evaluation of the Stirling Engine for Stationary Power Generation in the 500 to 2000 Horsepower Range*, ORO/5392-01, September, 1978, has many theoretical ramifications for the reader interested in engines development for solar use. The solar energy engines which have application for use in automobiles are still in the experimental (albeit workable) stage. The reader is cautioned to understand that the energy component descriptions, identifications, and speculations commented on in this section are to be considered within the framework of experimental theory and rough sketches of the theoretically possible. The fact that some things are indeed possible was highlighted in a 1978 article by E. F. Lindsley entitled, "60-Cycle AC from Sunshine, Solar Stirling Engine," in *Popular*

Science magazine. The Stirling engine takes its name from Robert Stirling, a Scotch clergyman, who in 1816, developed an engine that could be powered by any heat source. William Beale of Sunpower, Inc., in Athens, Ohio, has developed a Stirling engine/generator that appears to suggest considerable promise for future development. The reader may wish to review the U.S. government documents on Stirling engines and theory relating to it. Perhaps there are no real impossibilities to practical solar powered autos if sufficient research effort were focused on minimizing and resolving such disadvantages and difficulties as do exist. In part, it is simply a matter of priorities.

It is not really difficult to realize that the largest power factory of any type is, in reality, a model of "an engine," and that any power plant which exists has real potential for being miniaturized to act as an "engine" of suitable size for a specific need or requirement. True, in degrees of miniaturization, the compounding problem is how to maximize the needed power in the components of the engine or "power plant," but *that is precisely what our bright scientists have done* throughout the development of industrialized civilization. And we *can* develop a solar powered engine of acceptable size to run our cars. True, it will take experimentation and much refinement, but it already can be done far better than many people realize.

The United States Energy Research and Development Administration has a most readable document entitled, "Solar Program Assessment: Environmental Factors, Solar, Thermal, Electric," (ERDA 77-47/4 UC-11, 59, 62, 63A). This excellent document points out that the basic concepts solar thermal electric power generation requires, is the performance of the following functions:

1. Collection of solar energy;
2. Conversion of solar energy to thermal energy;
3. Thermal energy transport to an electric

energy converter;

4. Conversion of the thermal energy to electric energy;

5. Rejection or utilization (in the case of total energy systems) of thermal energy not used in the conversion process; and

6. Energy storage of backup systems to cover periods when direct solar radiation is not available.

The central receiver system need consist of five main subsystems:

1. Collector/concentrator subsystem;

2. Receiver/heat transfer subsystem;

3. Electric power generation subsystem (EPGS);

4. Thermal storage subsystems; and

5. A back-up or auxiliary system to insure adequate utility system reserve.

Beale's Solar Powered
Version Of
The Stirling Engine

I would like to comment briefly on what William Beale of Sunpower, Inc. apparently did. Beale's solar powered version of the Stirling engine reportedly uses a reflector focus to focus the sun's rays on the engine. This energy is then concentrated in an intensely hot spot and delivered to the absorber cavity of the sealed cylinder. This heat heats the high-pressure helium gas within. Inside, the power piston shuttles in a dependable, consistent 60 Hz rhythm. Electrical leads bring the power out ready for transmission to the user. The energy conversion takes place when the solar heat is transformed to mechanical energy to electrical power, and this is accomplished all within the sealed capsule. Beale's Stirling engine/generator uses only two moving parts. These are a displacer piston and a power piston. These moving parts operate in the capsule containing the intensely pressurized helium gas. The power piston doubles as an armature. As the power piston shuttles back and forth, it acts as the moving element in the electrical generation process. The operation, outlined, is reported thus:

1. Heat is applied to the outside of a sealed engine chamber (major component of a Stirling engine).

2. In the chamber, a pressurized gas shuttles back and forth between the heated space and a cooling chamber.

3. During this cycle, the gas expands and contracts to drive a set of pistons.

4. The displacer piston and power piston operate within the intensely pressurized helium gas chamber.

5. The power piston doubles as an armature. As it moves back and forth, it acts as the moving element in the electrical generation process.

The basic principles utilized above, in this case by William Beale, are utilized by others in developing heat engines to convert energy to electricity (see Farrington Daniels, *Direct Use of the Sun's Energy*) in developing solar engines. Dr. Daniels states, in discussing principles of solar engines:

"As in all heat engines, a fluid is made to expand by absorbing heat at a high temperature and to contract by liberating heat at a lower temperature. The mechanical work produced in the expansion moves a reciprocating piston in a cylinder or rotates a turbine wheel. Frequently, the mechanical work is converted into electrical work by means of a dynamo operating at a high efficiency of 90 per cent or more. The thermodynamic principles and the engineering studies were well developed many years ago." (p. 183 *op. cited*)

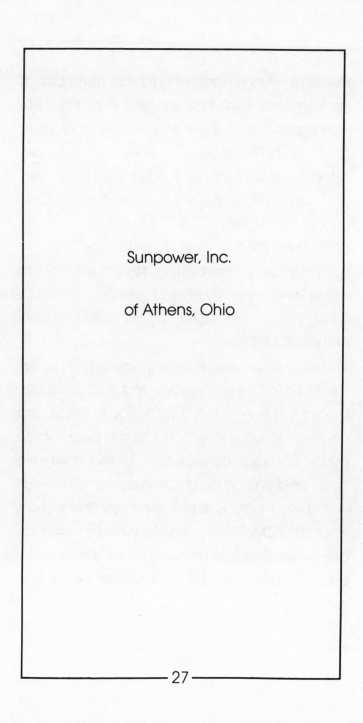

Sunpower, Inc.

of Athens, Ohio

PERSPECTIVE

The diminishing supply and rapidly rising cost of conventional fuels has made the prospect of maintaining and increasing the global standard of living more and more dependent on developing environmentally sound, cost effective, socially appropriate sources of energy. One important aspect of this challenge involves designing efficient and durable machinery to both conserve the existing fossil fuels and to utilize renewable sources of energy.

BACKGROUND

In 1964, William Beale, then an associate professor at Ohio University, invented and later patented the free piston adaptation of the Stirling engine, an engine which has the potential to make a major contribution in modifying life styles and energy production patterns in developing and industrialized societies. Some years later SUNPOWER, INC. was founded to accelerate the work of designing appropriate technologies for an energy future based on renewable resources.

BEALE FREE PISTON STIRLING ENGINE

The free piston Stirling engine has excellent thermodynamic efficiency — theoretically equal to Carnot. As an external heat engine it is capable of running on locally available fuel such as field waste, wood or coal, as well as on heat from direct sunlight. The free piston Stirling engine requires no lubrication, and, unlike crank drive Stirling engines, it is easily sealed, avoiding the almost impossible challenge of a long life moving seal. The free piston Stirling also has exceptionally high mechanical efficiency since it avoids the bearing and linkage drag of crank machines. It is also exceptionally quiet, making no more noise than an electric motor, and is very durable because there are so few parts to wear out. This combination of advantages and versatility make the free piston Sterling engine attractive as a remote area power source and as a promising decentralized energy technology.

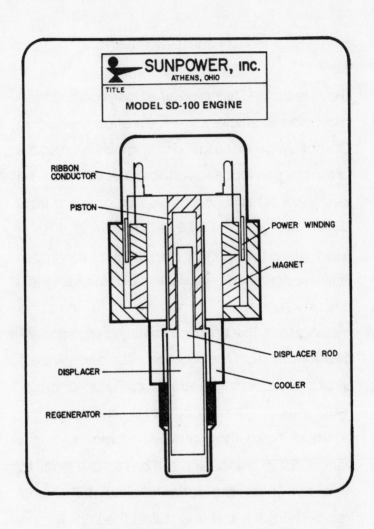

Courtesy: William Beale, Sunpower, Inc.

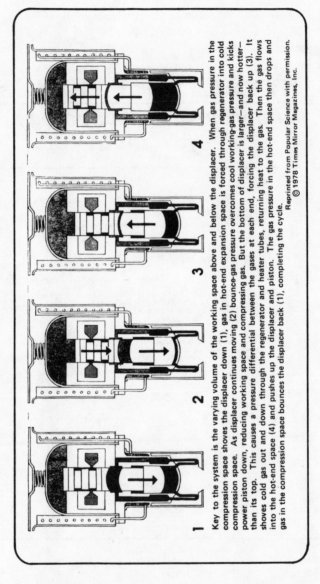

Key to the system is the varying volume of the working space above and below the displacer. When gas pressure in the compression space shoves the displacer down (1), gas in hot-end expansion space is forced through regenerator into cold compression space. As displacer continues moving (2) bounce-gas pressure overcomes cool working-gas pressure and kicks power piston down, reducing working space and compressing gas. But the bottom of displacer is larger—and now hotter—than its top. This causes a pressure differential between the gases at each end, forcing the displacer back up (3). It shoves cold gas out and down through the regenerator and heater tubes, returning heat to the gas. Then the gas flows into the hot-end space (4) and pushes up the displacer and piston. The gas pressure in the hot-end space then drops and gas in the compression space bounces the displacer back (1), completing the cycle.

Reprinted from Popular Science with permission.
© 1978 Times Mirror Magazines, Inc.

Courtesy: William Beale, Sunpower, Inc.

SOLAR ENERGY COLLECTORS
AND CONVERTERS

There are two kinds of devices which are used to intercept or to collect solar radiation and convert it to thermal energy. These are: (1) a Flat-plate Collector and (2) a Focus Collector.

FLAT-PLATE COLLECTORS

A flat-plate collector uses a blackened plate surface and tubes or fins arranged so that a fluid can pass by the plate and pick up heat from it. The fluid (e.g., water or air) is circulated as a carrying medium in thermal contact with the absorber plate. As it circulates it becomes heated (from contact with the flat absorber plate) and it is this heat which is further converted to be used in the next process. The flat-plate (absorber) itself may be any metal sheet which can incorporate water channels. It could, most simply, even be a model of an ordinary central heating radiator panel. There are many steel, copper, and aluminum products on the market which may be suitable. The fluid (e.g., water or air) channels must be connected in such a way (as, for example, at top and bottom) by some form of header or manifold. This manifold should ideally have a cross sectional area larger than the aggregate area of the channels served, to ensure a balanced and uniform flow in all channels. The surface finish of the flat-plate collector may be a matte black paint of a "chalkboard black" type and should have an appropriate rust inhibiting primer. The rust inhibiting primer should be of the wash-primer variety because a thick under-coat of paint would reduce the transmission. The primer must be of the self-etching type or must have equivalent qualities, or the repeated thermal expansion and contraction of the flat-plate collector will cause the paint to peel. Typically, the front side of the plate has one or more transparent covers that admit solar radiation as well as providing insulations. The back and sides of the flat-plate are also insulated to inhibit heat loss from the plate. The flat-plate collector is mounted in a fixed position, and absorbs both beam and diffuse radiation. Typically, flat-plate collectors can operate up to 125° F. (70° C.) above the daytime air temperature at the site of collection. Flat-plate collectors (radiation absorbers) may also be enclosed in a tray of some type (asbestos-cement, fiberglass, metal or wood) which incorporates a substantial thermal insulation at the back and edges (50-100 mm.) as well as holding a glass front. Such a complete unit may often be referred to as a "collector panel." Please note that flat-plate collectors may utilize both beam and diffuse solar radiation and are considered to be very practical devices. They are widely usable for water heating, house heating, air conditioning, evaporation of salt water, and in distillation of water for drinking purposes.

FOCUS COLLECTORS

In addition to flat-plate collectors which act as absorbers of solar radiation, another type of device is used called a Focus Collector, also sometimes referred to as a Concentrator or Concentrating Collector. Focusing or Concentrating Collectors are utilized when higher temperatures are required. These collectors use some form of optical concentration such as a concave reflector or lens to concentrate solar beam radiation, thereby raising its intensity from 2 to 10,000 times. As with flat-plate collectors, the focused or concentrated (magnified) radiation is abosrbed on a blackened receiver which is insulated to minimize thermal losses. The higher energy flux at the receiver allows energy collection at temperatures ranging from about 200° F. (100° C.) to about 5000° F. (2760° C.) or more. Focus collectors must be movable so that they can be oriented or mounted to track light somewhat in the manner of a "tracker" that can "search" and "lock" on target (radiation beams from the direction of the sun). The advantage of the focusing collector is not only the higher temperature produced but also the fact that while heat is gained from a large area, heat loss takes place only from the small surface of the actual absorber or plate collector.

The disadvantage of the Focusing Collector (concentrating device) is that they can only utilize the direct, directional radiation (beam radiation) from the sun. They do not respond to diffused radiant energy. The five basic types of focusing collectors which may be identified include the use of:

1. plane mirrors
2. parabolic troughs (which are cylindrical reflectors
3. parabolic reflectors
4. cylindrical Fresnel lenses
5. circular Fresnel lenses

Each of the above focus collector (etc.) devices has advantages and disadvantages. Additional research is needed to determine the best use of each device individually and in combination with one or another to determine maximum possible efficiency.

In addition to conversion of solar energy to thermal energy, it is possible to convert solar radiation directly into electricity by using two basic processes:

1. Thermo-electric conversion
2. Photo-electric conversion

Either of these processes has several forms well known to the technologist. Basically, when an electrode (a conductor used to establish electrical contact with a non-metallic part of a circuit) is heated a portion of its electrons will acquire enough energy to escape. The electrode acts as an electron-emitter, or *Cathode.* When another electrode is placed close to the cathode, if it is sufficiently cooled, it will act as a receiver of the emitted electrons and thus becomes or acts as an *Anode.* When the *anode* is connected to the *cathode* through a circuit containing an external load, a current will flow and "work" can be produced. Tungsten or Caesium-coated silver oxide may be used for electrode material. The electrodes are spaced at a distance of a fraction of a mm., in vacuo or in caesium vapour. There are many potential forms of generators for electrical conversion which include thermionic generators, thermocouples and thermopiles, photo-emissive generators, photo-galvanic generators (in a galvanic battery the potential difference changes when one of the electrodes is exposed to light), photo-diodes or photo-voltaic cells, etc. Efficiency factors vary and problems of efficiency still require solid research and experimental verification, but many materials have variable promise as semiconductors for use in solar cells. Some of these materials include germanium, silicon, indium phosphide, gallium arsenite, cadmium telluride, aluminum antimonide, cuprous oxide, selenium, gallium phosphide, cadmium sulphide and others. If these terms have unduly overwhelmed the reader, perhaps the reader will feel less overwhelmed to consider merely *silicon.* Consider the fact that silicon is defined as a tetravalent nonmetallic element that occurs combined as the most abundant element next to oxygen in the earth's crust and is used especially in alloys. Silicon occurs chiefly as *silica* or *sand*, which is silicon dioxide, and in the form of silicates. I think we will agree that there is a lot of this around. Its greatest use (elemental silicon) is as an alloying ingredient to strengthen aluminum, copper and magnesium. Silicon crystals are used in solar batteries and in the manufacture of semiconductor devices such as transistors and tunnel diodes. The reader may well have noted a bit of circularity in the past few sentences and

I hope so, for in spite of arguments over the relative weaknesses and/or strengths of certain semi-conductors, it should be obvious that some of these semi-conductors especially when utilized in conjunction with other materials, have the very basic property of serving as a reinforcing feedback element in certain types of generators. Anyway, would you believe something so basic as *sand* for a *solar cell?* Sunlight and sand! Think about it — sunlight and sand!

Overall, conversion of solar energy to electrical or mechanical energy is much more expensive than to convert solar energy to thermal energy. But necessity is the mother of invention and I, for one believe we have not resolved certain problems in this area simply because our governments and industries have not addressed themselves sufficiently to the problem on a scale sufficiently to fully resolve it. Does anyone seriously believe that government and industry which can send explorers to the far reaches of outer space and receive back from these explorers radar information in data and pictograph form — does anyone believe that the practical solar powered automobile presents unresolvable difficulties?

The solar cell is a solid-state device that directly converts the energy of solar radiation to electrical energy. The photoelectric cell (or electron tube) may be considered a form of such. Solar cells have largely been developed in order to provide electric power for spacecraft. Solar cells theoretically work in small sizes as well as in large sizes. They also work for very long periods of time with reasonable protection from damage. The applications for solar cell use include electric power supplies for radios, telephones, and communications equipment as well as power sources for lighthouses. Finally, heat engines may be used to convert solar energy to mechanical energy which is either used directly, or can be converted to electricity or electrical energy by the usual methods. In this operation, collectors may be utilized to heat a fluid (e.g., steam) which passes through an engine which converts a portion of the steam to mechanical energy. Very large flat-plate collectors are needed to raise the temperature of the fluid to achieve high levels of engine efficiency. Focus Collectors can more easily heat the fluids to the desired temperature level for maximum or desired engine efficiency level, but Focusing (concentrating) devices must be movable or have movable features to track and lock on the target of the solar beam. Remember, the Concentrating collector does not utilize the more generally available diffuse radiation.

This book does not intend to oversimplify some of the difficulties inherent at the present time in certain models of solar powered energy for automobiles. But we need to be realistic in realizing (and accepting) that in the beginning the available solar energy powered cars will have certain limitations that in time will be overcome during the process and experiment of

building and using solar energy powered automobiles. it would not seem to be realistic to put off their development until all the possible disadvantages be overcome. We achieve our goals by systematic approximation over time in reaching the desired ends in design and performance. That's where we may well need to begin with the solar-powered automobile.

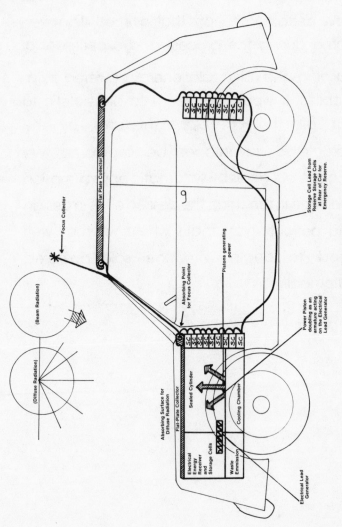

(Beam Radiation)

(Diffuse Radiation)

Absorbing Surface for
Diffuse Radiation

Flat-Plate Collector

Electrical
Energy
Receiver
and
Storage Cells

Sealed Cylinder

Waste
Emmission

Cooling Chamber

Electrical Lead
Generator

Focus Collector

Flat Plate Collector

Absorbing Point
for Focus Collector

Pistons generating
power

Power Piston
doubling as an
armature acting
on the Electrical
Lead Generator

Storage Cell Lead from
Reserve Storage Cells
at Rear of Car for
Emergency Reserve.

**ROUGH SCHEMATIC
OF SOLAR POWERED CAR.**

WHAT IS SOLAR ENERGY?

(THE NATURE OF SOLAR ENERGY)

Solar energy is radiated from the surface of the sun as a result of the Sun's continuous fusion process in which hydrogen nuclei combine to form helium nuclei. Since the mass of helium is less than the mass of hydrogen, some mass is always converted to energy which reaches the surface of the earth's atmosphere in the form of sunlight.

The wonderful thing about solar radiation is that it's an energy resource far, far greater than man's energy needs. For the most part, solar energy conversion as an energy product also offers the least potential damage with respect to environmental pollution. It also, once effectively harnessed, offers the greatest potential for providing inexpensive energy needs to the greatest number of people.

Only a very small fraction of the energy radiation from the sun is intercepted by the earth. A commonly quoted value of the average intensity of this radiation on the surface of the earth's atmosphere (93 million miles or 149.67 million km. from the sun) is 1.36 kilowatts per square meter (or 436 Btu/hr. ft.$_2$). This value is known as the solar constant. The solar constant is not a true constant, but varies by only 1% or 2% from year to year.

The solar constant as a unit of measurement may be defined as the number of calories received in one minute on one square centimeter or 0.15 square inch of the outer surface of the earth's atmosphere when the sun is about 93 million miles away. An accepted value of the solar constant is two calories. One calorie is the amount of heat energy needed to raise one gram of water by 1° C.

Solar energy from the sun is reflected, scattered and absorbed by the earth's atmosphere. Solar energy reaches the earth's surface, or the ground in one of two forms: (1) diffuse radiation or (2) beam radiation. In diffuse radiation the radiation comes from many directions whereas in beam radiation, the radiation comes from the direction of the sun. On clear, sunny days, the atmosphere may effectively transmit 90% of the solar radiation whereas on cloudy days as little as 10% of the radiation may be transmitted. Any serious plans involving the use of solar energy must take this variability into serious consideration and plan for effective storage reserve potential during maximum radiation periods for use on those occasions during which solar radiation is lessened or minimal.

Solar energy which reaches the ground has an intensity maximum of about 1.2 kilowatts per square meter, or about 1.3 horsepower per square yard. Nearly 50% of this solar energy is visible light, 50% is near infrared radiation while a minute percentage is found in the form of ultraviolet radiation. The nature of the sunlight (visible, infrared, ultraviolet) is important for solar energy considerations because each has different potential for energy conversion value.

Most readers need not be reminded that one of nature's most basic processes is the conversion of solar radiation to chemical energy in the form of photosynthesis in plants. Furthermore, photosynthesis is nature's means by which all of our conventional fuels have been produced, the products being modified and stored in nature as wood, coal, natural gas and oil, or in other materials derived from plant residue. It has taken, in most cases, "eons" of time to supply these fuel resources and they are fast running out because of the world's energy needs. Before we go on to consider how solar energy can be converted directly to thermal energy, let's consider some basic facts on the history of man's direct use of solar radiation for energy purposes. First of all, the Chinese, since ancient times, followed by the Egyptians, Phoenicians, Greeks, and Romans in their turn, are known to have used solar energy to evaporate salt water to product salt. Solar crop drying is an ancient art known to the most ancient civilizations. A major solar still was built at Las Salinas, Chile, in 1872. Egypt, in 1913, utilized a 13,269-square foot (1,233 square meter) parabolic collector which provided steam to run an engine for pumping irrigation water from the Nile River. In 1939, the Massachusetts Institute of Technology built one of the first solar-heated houses at Cambridge, Massachusetts. Practical flat-plate collectors (for solar radiation) were designed as early as 1942 through the experimental studies of the American scientists, H.C. Hottel and B. B. Woertz. The American scientists, D. M. Chapin, C. S. Fuller, and G. L. Pearson, were instrumental in developing successful silicon solar cells.

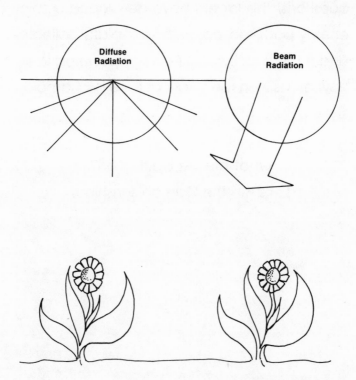

Photosythesis...natures most basic photochemical process, transforming solar energy to biochemical processes necessary to plant and animal life, the decay from which is ultimately natural gas, coal, etc.

Are solar energy powered cars in existence to-day? Have any been developed? Yes! to both questions. The Israelis have developed a solar energy-powered car with flat-plate collector under the hood! A solar energy-powered Rolls-Royce has won the solar car race in champion style.

What are we waiting on?
Let's run the Cars on sunshine!

APPENDIX

This appendix consists of a list of sources which the interested reader may refer to for solar information. These sources may have recently added or deleted suggested service, products or information but have been known to provide items of varied types related to solar technology during the past several years. The items listed are not conclusive of the offerings and the reader is urged to write the company for full information of services and full range of products.

1. Aluminum Company of America
    1501Alcoa Building
    Pittsburgh, PA 15219

    Solar collector parts
    Solar collectors
    Optical coatings

2. Crypton Optics, Inc.
    7 Skillman Street
    Roslyn, N.Y. 11576

    Fresnel lenses

3. Spectrolab
   12484 Gladstone Avenue
   Sylmar, CA 91342

   Solar cell banks

4. Solarex Corp.
   1335 Picaard Drive
   Rockville, MD 20850

   Solar powered battery chargers
   Solar cell banks
   Solar cell charge controllers
   Solar cells

5. Solar Energy Digest
   P.O. Box 1776
   San Diego, CA 92177

   Solar publications

6. Solar Energy Research and Information
   Center
   1001 Connecticut Avenue, Suite 632
   Washington, D.C.

   Solar publications

7. PPG Industries, Inc.
   One Gateway Center
   Pittsburgh, Pennsylvania 15222

   Solar collectors

8. National Aeronautics and Space
    Administration (NASA)
    Technology Utilization Office
    George C. Marshall Space Flight Center
    Marshall Space Flight Center, AL 35812

    Solar publications

9. Edmund Scientific Co.
    555 Edscorp,
    New Jersey, NJ 08007

    In addition to parabolic mirrors, solar cell
    banks, solar cells and many of the usual
    solar products, this company has had
    available solar cigarette lighters!

10. Tranter, Inc.
    Plate Coil Division
    735 Hazel Street
    Lansing, MI 48909

    Solar collectors

11. J. A. Duffie
    University of Wisconsin
    Engineering Experimental Station
    1500 Johnson Drive
    Madison, WI 53706

    John A. Duffie is one of the leading world authorities on solar energy and the principles underlying its utilization. He has provided outstanding theoretical and research contributions in solar radiation theory, solar flat-plate collectors, solar focus collectors and their design and performance as well as solar energy storage. He has served as director and is affiliated with the solar energy laboratory at the University of Wisconsin.

12. Daniels, Farrington; *Direct Use of the Sun's Energy*, Yale University Press (1964) Ballantine Books, 1974, Division of Random House, New York, New York

13. Mr. William Beale
    Sunpower, Inc.
    Athens, Ohio

14. U.S. Department of energy *Stirling Engine Report* September, 1978; ORO/5392-01 *A Technological Evaluation of the Stirling Engine for Stationary Power Generation in the 500 to 2000 Horsepower Range.*

15. U.S. Department of Energy; Division of Solar Energy. *Proceedings of the Solar Thermal Concentrating Collector Technology Symposium* by Gypta, B. P. and F. Kreith (Eds.) held in Denver, Colorado, June 14 and 15, 1978; August 1978. Department of Energy Contract No. EG-77-C-01-4042.

16. U.S. Department of Energy, Office of Energy Technology; Division of Central Solar Technology. *Handbook of Data On Selected Engine Components for Solar Thermal Applications. June, 1979.*

Pyramid

I,
Ra,
The
Sun God
And the chief
Deity of Historical
Egypt, do shine with
Power yet over the ancient
Land and bless with my golden
Rays that lesser god, the crocodile
Who lives in the mud and water of the
River Nile in the Sacred fertile valley of
The land which honored my golden eye and I,
Who see and know all things, yet harbor the
Secret of the labor of the timeless pyramids with
All the mystery of their making; their glorious undertaking
By a people who were enamored of and empowered by, The Sun.

To help you along your path toward alternative fuels, I am listing some useful books. All the following books may be ordered at the prices indicated from: Love Street Books, P.O. Box 58163, Louisville, Kentucky 40258 U.S.A. For shipping charges, add 75¢ for the first book and 35¢ for each additional book.

ALTERNATIVE ENERGY BOOKS

FORGET THE GAS PUMPS — MAKE YOUR OWN FUEL. By Jim Wortham and Barbara Whitener. A pressure cooker, some copper coils, cooling and catch basin for distillate of fermented corn sugar, yeast, and water give you 160 proof alcohol, produced on stovetop or in the backyard. Wortham and Whitener illustrate carburetor and choke adjustments so any beginner can do it. Fermentation recipes and sample fuel distiller's permit included. **Price $3.95.**

CONVERT YOUR CAR TO ALCOHOL. By Keat Drane. With this manual you'll find everything you need to know about converting your family car to alcohol. Using a Dodge Dart, the author wanted to prove to himself and others that any car can run on straight alcohol, without gasoline! This book is illustrated with photos showing the actual conversion, step-by-step. Parts purchased for conversion are listed and costs tabulated. Those with little or no mechanical experience can follow. **Price $4.95.**

SOLAR FUEL — HOW TO MAKE AUTOMOTIVE FUEL USING YOUR OWN ALCOHOL SOLAR STILL. By Dennis Smith. This book is the comprehensive solar still handbook. Smith illlustrates with photos and blueprint drawings how to construct a solar still using items lying around the house. Home production of alcohol, tuning a car for alcohol, and getting a government permit included. **Price $4.95.**

ELECTRIC CAR BOOK. By Barbara Whitener. The author explores conversion of the conventional vehicle to electric power. Exciting advantages of this alternative are discussed. Drawings and photos included. **Price $4.95.**

RUN YOUR CAR ON SUNSHINE: USING SOLAR ENERGY FOR A SOLAR POWERED CAR. By James Neal Blake, Ph.D. The author reveals a suppressed concept. He tells how to eliminate fuel completely by using sunshine to power a car. Includes illustrations. **Price $6.95.**